The Canal of the Midi
& Pierre-Paul Riquet

Original title : Le Canal du Midi et Pierre-Paul Riquet,
© Édisud, Aix-en-Provence, 1993.

ISBN 2-85744-675-6
© C.-Y. Chaudoreille, Édisud, Aix-en-Provence, 1993.

The Canal of the Midi & Pierre-Paul Riquet

History of the "Canal royal en Languedoc"

Text and photographs by
JACQUES MORAND

Translated from the original French by
Adam R. Tolkien

Édisud
La Calade, 13090 Aix-en-Provence, France

CONTENTS

I
THE REASONS OF A BIRTH

Three centuries already !

Pierre-Paul Riquet died on the Second of october 1680 ; Baron of Bonrepos, he was the creator of the Royal Canal of Languedoc, the modern-day "Canal du Midi", also known as the Canal of Two Seas.

On the 15th of May 1681, the Canal was opened to navigation and on the 18th of the same month it was inaugurated by the highest authorities of the Province, with all the pomp and decorum of the time.

The towns of the Southwest have always quarrelled over who should reap the glory of the genius who was able to join the waters of that amazing water-tower, last buttress of the Massif Central, the Black Mountain, then masterfully direct them towards the watershed of the Seuil de Naurouze, below the first rises of the Pyrenees and, from there, to feed each branch of the Canal, towards the Atlantic and the Mediterranean.

Béziers, his birthplace, erected a statue in his honour and named a square after him. Toulouse also has produced its statue, its Boulevard Bonrepos, its Riquet Street. Revel, where he stayed, Castelnaudary, Agde, all these towns have acknowledged "nostre Riquet", child of the region.

Every day, thousands of people follow or cross the Royal Canal of Languedoc, which has since become the Canal of the Midi, with the negligence of familiarity ; they live on a Riquet Street, or write the name Bonrepos, only attaching some fragmentary vision the work or the name. One must have travelled the length of the Canal du Midi, one must have seen the Mountain Channel, the Cammazes, the dam of Saint-Ferréol or the crossing of the Malpas, to be able to measure the size of this work, a grandiose project that was executed over 300 years ago, that has remained intact over time, without a wrinkle and still as functional as ever.

The Canal of the Midi was born of the encounter of two exceptional men: Pierre Paul Riquet, Farmer of the Gabelles, and Colbert, Controller of finances under King Louis the XIVth.

Aided by the approval and support of Louis the XIVth, the most considerable work of the century was realized in record time. It used all of the techniques

Revel

known at the time in hydrography, topography, geometry, public works and architecture, it even used notions of ecology, saving certain locations, adjusting the forestry by planting over 45 000 trees in the first years of its exploitation.

Colbert's support and arbitration, watching over France's economic power and reputation, allowed the putting into practice of original formulas of tutelage by making the Canal into a fief, the last application of a disappearing feudal law. Accepting Riquet's proposals in financing, guaranteeing his loans from the States of Languedoc, backing him with an understanding, effective and very much ahead of its time administration, very surprising in its adaptability and modernity, Colbert exploited Riquet's capabilities to their utmost.

In spite of obstacles, incomprehension and hesitation, the largest project of this type embarked upon in France at the time was superbly realized with the sense of grandeur that was inherent to the century.

"Did not the soul of the King prefer, even in functional things, those that carry the character of greatness." (Colbert)

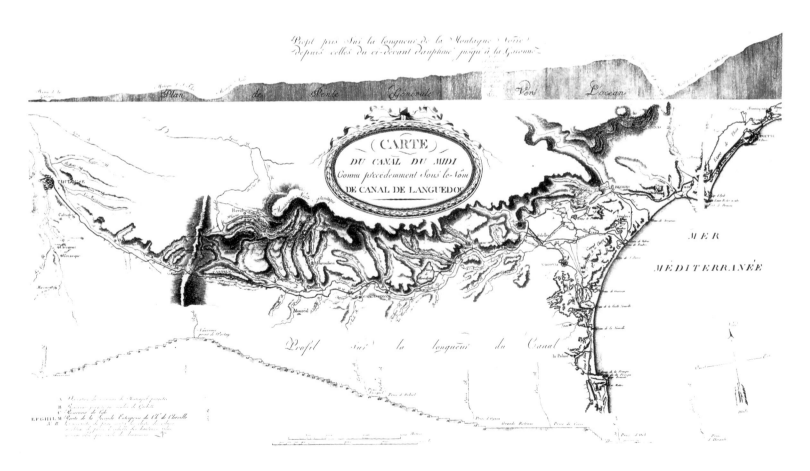

Still, this realization remains the work, the creation of one man, of its promoter : Pierre-Paul Riquet. His tenacity enabled him to surmount all obstacles, whether financial or technical, to surmount resentment and envy and treachery. To this opus he sacrificed his belongings, his health, and he never saw the completion of his work. He gave himself entirely to this great design. He was an Adventurer, in the noble sense of the word, totally absorbed in a work that still astounds in its audacity.

Like the builders of Rome, he has marked the province, the country and towns, with his seal. It can thus truly be said of him that, through his genius and the sheer size of his work, he was the last of the Romans.

France at the beginning of the reign of Louis the XIVth

Louis the XIVth began his reign over a country that was ending a civil war, the "Fronde" — the last revolt of an aristocracy trying to oppose the triumphant march of absolutism — as well as a war with Spain. Finally, in 1659, Philip the IVth, King of Spain, accepted peace : France signed the Treaty of the Pyrenees, and the young King married Theresa of Austria on the 6th of June 1669.

He found himself reigning over a heterogeneous and archaic country, where royal power was still constrained by solid feudal traditions. The royal treasury was low, much money was needed to satisfy the needs of politics and of war, that had created the usual troubles : armies living off the land, burning, pillaging, killing and producing a dramatic famine following the catastrophic harvests of 1657 and 1662. In the country, people were eating acorns, bark, bread made with flour mixed with clay and nettle soup. The Languedoc, where the Canal was to be dug, was faring no better than the other provinces. A region *"rich in population and in land"*, it was a poor relation in the recovery that was on its way.

There are two Languedocs : High Languedoc and Low Languedoc.

Basville, in his "Memoirs to serve in the History of the Languedoc", depicts them as *"two countries, differing in the quality of the land, in the genius and actual nature of their inhabitants"*. In High Languedoc the land is fertile. Wheat grows well, as well as fruit. Vines are little developed. The inhabitants are crude, slow workers and have very little industry.

In Low Languedoc, the land is poorer and more varied. Grain grows badly, there is little cattle breeding, apart from sheep and goats. The only riches consist in the vineyards. It is not yet a monoculture, but this traditional activity is in constant development. Olive trees are still to be found around Montpellier, saffron and pastel around Toulouse. There are some industries : Nîmes is the center of the silk industry ; Montpellier that of wool ; sheets are made in Carcassonne. This diversification of activities means that the attitude of the population is different : they are livelier and more active.

High and Low Languedoc are thus complementary and in contrast with the region of Aquitaine, where the import of foreign capital and the trade in the port of Bordeaux allows for a high level of activity : excedent wine, vinegar and eau-de-vie is exported ; from Gascony, resin, colophane, turpentine and honey. The interior provinces supply red meat, pork and geese for exportation. Allowing for this abundance, Bordeaux is lacking in wheat and must import it. Trade should thus logically be installed between Aquitaine and Languedoc, but no. Commerce in Aquitaine is directed towards the Atlantic, that of the Languedoc towards the Mediterranean. This division being due to the geography of the area, ancient political divisions and reciprocal and egotistical protectionism.

Also, the isolation of the region of Languedoc is due to the absence of means of communication : with no roads, olives are carried from Montpellier to Toulouse by mule !

This situation is a result of the indifference of the States of Languedoc towards public works, roads being dependent on the initiative of the dioceses and seneschalsy. The only means of transport through Languedoc are the boats on the Garonne and Aude rivers. The joining of Toulouse and Bordeaux along the Garonne is precarious, the waters being too low for navigation between may and october.

The state of the ports is no better, even allowing for various attempts at restoration. Every time, sand banks appear and choke the efforts that have been made : at Aigues-Mortes[1], the Grau Henry closed in 1610. Montpellier trades through Maguelonne and Palavas, bringing on an expensive breach of charges. Frontignan, in the basin of Thau, is the most active port, but the boats remain small (loads not exceeding 20 tons). Narbonne, two leagues from the sea, communicates with the small port of La Nouvelle, along the Robine, so badly-tended that it can only take very low-tonnage boats. An enquiry made in 1664 showed up the complete ruin of trade from Narbonne. This leaves Agde, a military port, accessible to galleys and defended

1. Dead Waters

by the Fort of Brescou, but also threatened by sand silting up.

The necessity for a real port to restore the maritime trade had already been percieved by the royal government. As early as 1596, Henry the IVth decided to embark upon the construction of a port in Sète, that would allow *"trading with large vessels that are otherwise obliged to travel to Marseilles or Genoa"*. The jetties were well advanced when the work was abandoned due to lack of resources. The States of Languedoc had refused to participate. There was nothing left by 1664. In 1656, the trading classes had produced complaints, recording the complete failure of commerce, the closing off of the Province to maritime traffic and pleading with the King to remedy the situation.

The idea of a canal, joining the Ocean and the Sea, to give an impulse to trading had been envisaged for a long time. This junction had another stake as well, a political and military one that had been brought to notice by Strabon. The English domination of Aquitaine had for a long time slowed the idea of a canal joining the two seas.

The beginning of a great reign

A blossoming of monarchic power made itself felt right from the beginning of the personal reign of Louis the XIVth.

Three men, from 1661 to 1671, participated in the royal power, seated in the King'shigh-counsel : Hughes de Lionne, Le Tellier, and Colbert. The rise of France remains especially the work of Colbert, whose first task was to be the re-establishment of the finances. Income was three years behind expenditure. Extraordinary measures had to be taken to recover the situation : thus, the establishment of a Chamber of Justice, to seek out the various abuses and misappropriations that had taken place over the preceding years and reduce overvalued annuities. Colbert also put into order and reorganized the administration of the finances, thus adding to the resources of the state and, for the first time, in 1675, the budget was balanced. Through his efforts, the raise in royal income managed to follow the expenditure : 32 million pounds in 1661, 93 million in 1663, while expenditure went from 53 million to 109 million. To be able to face this rise in expenditure without exhausting the kingdom other sources of income had to be found. France did not have the possibilities of a country like Spain to import gold and silver from the American colonies. Money must be attracted from elsewhere, and saved in the country. The eternal problem : how to produce more for export, at the time it was called Mercantilism.

France cut a sorry figure on the foreign markets, dominated as it was by the Dutch and the English and drowned by importation – 23 to 30 million pounds, against 12 to 18 million in export. The French were buying mirrors, glass and lace from Venice, bedding and cloth from Holland, tin from Germany, carpets from Persia, and agriculture counted for little on the world market.

To combat this state of affairs, Colbert was to institute an interventionist policy, implanting these industries in France : attracting foreign experts, loaning capital for the establishment of factories, alloting exemption from taxes or monopolies of production and sales. To raise the quality over that of other countries, he implemented very strict regulations, establishing norms and controls,

reorganizing the trade corporations. These policies, inspired by Mercantilism, bore the name of their instigator : Colbertism. He began a real economic war, also consisting of a complete plan of reorganization and repairing of the road and river system. The Royal Canal of Languedoc was part of this national plan, allowing trade and exchanges between East and West, Atlantic and Mediterranean.

Colbert systematically took control over the studies and direction of these works ; all officers in charge of highway maintenance, Treasurers of France, Superintendents, etc... were discharged in favor of Intendents that he nominated, bearing such names as Bosquet, Bazin, Bezons, Aguesseau, and Basville.

Previous projects and the science of canals

The idea of a canal joining the two seas and avoiding the perils of navigating around Spain was not new in 1666. The possibility had already been envisaged in Nero's time, and under Charlemagne.

The first real project was proposed to the King François the First. It would have joined the Aude and the Garonne. Two royal Commissioners examined the terrain between Toulouse and Villepinte, a small village near the small town of Castelnaudary ; it would have been a 50 mile long canal, arriving in the Fresquel, a small tributary of the river Aude, and passing into the Aude, whose bottom would be cleaned of rocks. The project was not viable, neither taking into account the irregular course of the Aude, nor the altitude of the threshold of Naurouze. A project was also established under Charles the IXth, but its course has not reached us through the barriers of time.

In 1598, Henry the IVth had a project drawn up, it was judged impossible by a famous engineer of the time, Louis of Foix.

On the 12th of January of the year 1618, the Assembly of States of Languedoc reviewed a canal project, the work of a native of Béziers, Bernard of Arribat, *"offering to supply the financing of the project and to ask nothing but that the work were to be finished"*. The States of Languedoc cavalierly rejected the proposal, with the pretext that they had no time to deliberate on the subject.

After 1630, other more or less practical projects were submitted. In 1663, Bauvau planned a canal between the Garonne and the Aude. Another, anonymous, project was to lead the waters of the river Ariège to the Faubourg Saint-Michel in Toulouse, thus feeding the canal as far as Trèbes. The last one to date, in 1650, would have taken water from the Ariège, 20 miles from Toulouse, at Cintegabelle, and led a canal to Trèbes and the river Aude, 5 miles from Carcassonne. None of these projects took into account the elevation of the Naurouze threshold, the state of the riverbeds or the lack and irregularity of water debit ; indeed, the science of canal-building was limited at the time to the conception of simple or lock canals.

The Garonne at Toulouse

In the case of simple diversion, the canal maintains a constant level, or a very gentle slope to lead the waters from one point to another. There must be no obstacles, such as a rise in the land or a heavy slope between the two points. This being the ancient principle, taken up again by the Italians in the Middle-Ages for the Tinicello, diverting off the Tessino.

The system has been applied, in particular in Zeeland, to drain the lands and make them cultivable : at low tide, the on land waters are higher than sea level ; the gates are opened for the water to flow out ; they are then closed when the tide returns to avoid a reflux.

The invention of the double-lock, or airlock, is attributed to Leonardo da Vinci, but some authors would have it that Peter and Dominic Viterbe, engineers of the Republic of Venice, used the system for the first time at Stra, near Padua, towards 1491. It is known that Leonardo da Vinci applied it in 1497 on the diversion canals of the rivers Adda and Tessino, and that he introduced it to France during his stay in the courts of François the First. Though the double lock allows the canal to cross a larger difference in altitude, without adding to the slope of the canal bed, it does not permit the surmounting of obstacles such as the Naurouze threshold, without special adaptation. The solution being the separation point canal : feeding the canal from the highest point of the profile, this ascertains continuity on each slope. This definitive step ahead in the science of canal-building was made by Adam de Craponne, a Provençal gentleman, the creator of an irrigation canal from the Durance to the Étang de Berre. He proposed the application of this principal to link the two seas.

The system was used for the first time on the Canal of Briare. The feeding of the canal was realized by diverting rivers and ponds, and assembling them *"at the highest points, called the separation-point, because, from there, the waters flow down two opposite slopes"*. Designed to link the Seine and the Loire, the canal of Briare was the first important work of this type to be executed in Europe, where lock-canals where built only to allow boats to move in both directions. It was begun in 1605, under the direction of the engineer Hughes de Cosnier, *"a man very much ahead of his time by more than a century... who conceived and executed"*. He perfected the technique, placing more than one lock side by side as the difference in altitude grew. The death of Henry the IVth and Sully's departure brought on the ceasing of work. It was taken up again, by Guillaume Bouteroue and Jacques Guyon, in 1638 on a grant from Louis the XIIIth, and finished in 1642.

All the conditions that were to allow the "Canal du Midi" to see the light of day seemed to come together at the beginning of the reign of Louis the XIVth. The new King was a man of high aims. He wished to engage France in a true renewal. His plan *"is for commerce to flourish in the kingdom by such considerable advantages"*, as he wrote in the preamble of "the Edict for the construction of a communication canal between the two seas, Ocean and Mediterranean", given in Saint-Germain-en-Laye, in October 1666. The new minister, Colbert, undertook a policy of industrial expansion, backing it up with public works : roads, ports and waterways that were necessary for the circulation of goods and wealth.

Since Briare, canals could be built ; the technique of crossing the separation line was now tried and tested. Previous projects had shown the difficulties and problems to be resolved. Only the water was lacking ; the water without which the project could only remain a project.

The three necessary conditions for the realization of the project had been brought together : the State wished for it, the technique had been mastered, water had been found to aliment it.

Indeed, Riquet's stroke of genius was to find this water in the "Montagne Noire", the Black Mountain and constrain and direct it to Naurouze, then to personally conduct and finance the largest work of the century.

II
PIERRE-PAUL RIQUET, BARON OF BONREPOS

His origins and youth, a Gabelle farmer

Who was this providential man, whose exceptional qualities allowed the realization of a so considerable work ? Who was this man, capable of engaging his honour and fortune in the conception and execution of an adventure that ended at the same time as his very life ?

Pierre-Paul Riquet was born in Béziers on the 29th of June 1604 or 1609, on the feast day of the Saints Peter and Paul, whose names he bore.

It is supposed that he died on the 2nd of October 1680 in Toulouse, where he is buried in the Saint-Étienne Cathedral.

His origins are less of a mystery.

His family was qualified as "very noble and very ancient", a family tree has been kept in the archives of the Canal. The family originated in Florence. It has been traced back as far as the XIIth Century, with a florentine family named Arrighetti, one of whose members was a Consul of the City in 1197. A standard-bearer and

eleven "Freedom priors" were also recruted from the family, while Florence was a republic. The War of the Guelfs and the Gibelins brought about the emigration of the family. The execution in Naples, in 1268 after his defeat at the Battle of Taglia-Cozzo, of Conradin, last of the Hohenstanfers, was to lead to the flight of the Gibelin Party, fearing the threat of Charles of Anjou.

Gherardo Arrighetti was bannished from Florence for having followed the Gibelin party. He took refuge in Provence, where he found a little of his homeland. He was to install himself successfully, gallicizing his name to Riquetti, or Riquety.

His grandson, Pierre Riquetty, left his mark as first Consul in the Council of La Seyne, in 1346. He is designated in certain acts as "Nobilis Dominus Petrus Riquety".

Skipping some generations, we find Antoine Riquety, who died in 1508. During the XVth century, the family split into two branches : the one staying in Provence, and the other, moving to the Languedoc, and francizing their name further to Riquet.

Nicholas, the grandson of Antoine, was a master tailor in Béziers, where he held a fabric shop. On the 29th of August 1565, he married Beatrix Bordier, the daughter of the nobleman, Jean Bordier, with whom he begat five or six children ; amongst whom was Guillaume, Pierre-Paul Riquet's father.

It is impossible to evoke Guillaume Riquet without halting awhile on this character, and his colorful personality and life. His tailor of a father gave him a solid, if not good, education, he was a solicitor in Béziers until 1618. Being at the time part of the political life of the town and assisting at the meetings of the General assembly, he was able to vote against Arribat's aforementioned canal project. In 1611 he took against the Consuls in place, and quarreled with the first Consul, going so far as to *"punch him in the shoulder and threatening to grievously exceed"*.

Around this time he sold his practice to a Raymond Dedieu, so as to acquire a prosecutor's office in the court of Béziers, which had him condemned before the Parliament of Toulouse *"for vicious and deleted retainers, forged writings with altered dates"*. This was not the first time he had trouble with the law and after the sale of his practice he embarked in "business", of the kind that denounces both the trafficker and the profiteer, that was to enrich him considerably, the period being ripe for this manner of livelihood.

This ex-solicitor-come-businessman was *"intelligent, intuitive, daring, with little or no scruples, all the required qualities for fiddling"*. He started in speculation : first with money loans ; then trafficking in grain and seed, accepting advances and payment in kind, that he would then sell later with large profits. He took up a partnership to furnish Béziers in lamb meat. With two partners, Lys de Bugnes and Pierre Amilhon, he realized a sort of trust of the Clerking offices of the town. He also managed the Central Butchery, the drying out of the Lake of Capestan, the collection of the produce of the dioceses of Languedoc.

Guillaume Riquet was an enterprising man, a skilful businessman, a sort of banker, actively participating in the financial and political life of Béziers.

All this activity must have affected Pierre-Paul Riquet's education. It formed in him the spirit of enterprise and boldness of a man of finance with the qualities of a leader of men. He got from his father *"that mixture of common sense and imagination, that taste for action that characterized him"*.

We know little about his youth : did he follow classes at the Collège of Béziers ? He said of himself, that he gave little satisfaction to his teachers, and preferred the language of Oc to French : *"I have a little nature and no art"*. In a letter to Colbert, he admits to not having greek or latin, the basis of any serious studies at the time ; only Science and Mathematics seem to have interested him. Because of this he could neither follow in his fathers steps as prosecutor, nor embrace a profession.

His godfather, François de Portugniares, got him into the Gabelle farm [2], and he became the Languedoc sub-farmer in 1651. He showed himself to be very capable and to have particular talent in the domain of financing. He took up the supplying of the King's armies in Cerdagne and Roussillon, this activity allowing him to accumulate a large fortune estimated to have been over a million pounds.

2. The Gabelle was a tax on salt, put into practice during the XIIIth century, that represented an important source of income to the state. The nobility, clergy and certain Provinces were exempted from the tax : all others were obliged to buy a certain amount of salt from the salt lofts and "Officers of the Gabelle".

Riquet married, probably when he was 19, Catherine de Milhau, the daughter of a bourgeois of Béziers, they were to beget five children.

We have no indications on the appearance of the young Riquet. The portrait painted by Sébastien Bourdon (1616-1671) is already that of a developed man and shows us an appearance closer to that of a churchman of the previous century than a Gabelle farmer. A musketeers beard and moustache, a slightly sardonic smile that goes with the expression of the eyes, his face seems placed on a collar of two huge white flaps, spreading out onto his robe. One might think one were looking at a cardinal de Retz or Mazarin, if it were not for the simplicity of the costume. A strong impression of intelligence escapes from the portrait ; the compass in his hand is a reminder of Riquets vocation.

The statue erected in his honour, at the top of the Jean-Jaurès alleys in Toulouse, sculpted by Griffoul-Dorval, presents us with an older man, dressed according to the fashion of the time, very Louis XIV : a curled wig, a slightly open jacket, showing jabot and lace sleeves, French breeches with tights and buckled shoes, a large cape thrown over his shoulder. Dressed carefully, but without frills. The character is massively built, and gives off an air of security and maturity. This is the man who invented the Canal. His face is serious, barred by a thin moustache, breathing authority, *"an attentive look along with deep interior meditation".* His cleft chin is that of a headstrong man. But, looking carefully, one also notices an air of tiredness that he is trying to hide : he is carrying on his shoulders the heaviest construction of the century, and from time to time doubt and fatigue must make their presence felt. Is he not constantly the prey of financial difficulties, jealousy, incomprehension and the petty treasons of

his close collaborator, the engineer François d'Andreossy ?

The adventurer

True qualities were united in this man that made the autodidact into an adventurer, not in the pejorative, but in the noble sense of the word :

– His mind had to be open enough to be interested in problems of hydrology and hydrography, even given his lack of training and the distance from his work with the Gabelle tax.

– He was bold enough to present his project to a personage of the grandeur of Colbert, then to realize the first work on the Montagne Noire with his own money, to prove the validity of his plan.

– He had a sense for economic and financial problems that allowed him to construct a viable project ; Colbert would never have authorized Riquet to embark on the work if he hadn't, after resolving the technical problems, been able to bring financial solutions to light.

– He must also have had an extraordinary sense of organization for the time ; at certain times, he had up to 12 000 workers under his orders, and it only took him 14 years to complete his project as far as the Basin of Thau, and start work on the port of Sète.

– He must finally have had a feeling for technical innovation, realizing as he did the first mass-dam in Europe, and the first canal-bridge, also piercing a tunnel through the mountain at Malpas, near Béziers.

A dominant part of his character was sincerity ; there was no duplicity or lying in his relationships. In his letters to Colbert he never tried to hide his situation or smooth over his difficulties : *"I am in a violent state, this is my whole fortune"*, he wrote on the 25th of May 1676, letting him know the state his finances were in, because he was being paid late !

Colbert gave him his support, but not always unreservedly, or without wariness. He delegated De La Feuille to "assist" him and check the work, while assuring Riquet of his confidence in him.

Riquet was also a solitary type, and obstinate. Of course, he was surrounded by engineers such as Andreossy, the Chevalier of Clerville, father Mourgues, even Vauban, for certain structures. But he always ended up imposing his point of view or personal decision, sometimes by presenting the others with the fait accompli, and always refused to share important responsabilities. For these reasons his enterprise always remained in the family, without foreign capital. He only ever took up partnership with his son Jean-Mathias, and his inheritors stayed with this conception in the administration of the Canal.

All the same, Riquet remained a financier in this venture, keeping in mind his own wealth. Though he made sacrifices and risked what he already had, along with his health, he knew that the Canal would be wealth for his family. From the beginning, when he proposed to Colbert that he should build the feeding channel to Naurouze with his own money, he was already suggesting that *"if I succeed happily, I shall have cause to pretend to being well paid for my forfeit, and I pray you humbly accord me your suffrages, so that may acquire honour and some goods"*.

He never doubted in the success of his venture, his faith was unshakeable.

When he began the construction of the canal, Riquet was worth more than a million pounds ; he had "arrived" :

The source of his fortune can be explained by the property that had been left to him by his father, and by his gains as a Gabelle farmer and supplier of the kings armies. However, he will be led to advancing millions of pounds, in the course of the construction. Though Riquet was, in modern day terms, a multi-millionaire, there is a marked disrepancy between his wealth in 1666 and the sums that he would then manipulate and dispose of on his own account.

On the 5th of August 1670, he bought the County of Caraman from the marquis Paul d'Escoubleau de Sourdis who was in debt. He bought it for his youngest son, and as the Barony of Saint-Félix was dependent on the County, it enabled the owner to sit at the Languedoc States.

In 1677, his eldest son, Jean-Mathias, who had been a counsellor in the Parliament since 1664, wished to buy for himself an office as Master of Appeals. The price was too high for him ; the office costed 150 000 pounds ! He solicited his father, who promptly came up with the sum.

Riquet was perpetually in the red, and at one point tried to borrow 300 000 pounds from the States of Languedoc.

For some this steady, calculated and systematic social and financial rise remains a financial mystery.

But Riquet's fortune can mainly be explained by the man's character : he was an untiring worker with strong imaginative faculties, he was bold, obstinate, enthusiastic, he was observant, and with his good judgement was capable of using situations to his profit.

Everything about him was geared towards social rising and financial success : he wanted to be a nobleman ; acquiring the land of Bonrepos did not give him a title, it was only the construction of the canal that would bring him this success that he felt dated back to his Florentine ancestors, the Arrighetti family. This was possible as the King erected the Canal into a fief, one of the last manifestations of this feudal right, fast becoming obsolete.

Riquet knew that he was the inventor of the canal, that he had discovered the means to realize it ; this invention should thus be his property. He asked to be responsible for the construction of the canal, for rendering it perfectly navigable and for its upkeep on these conditions : that the Canal and its dependencies should be erected as a haubert fief, and should thus become his property, with the right to build buidings and mills, the fief also having the right of high and low justice.

So, it would seem that fortune smiled on Pierre-Paul Riquet's enterprise : inventor of the canal, in charge of the rapidly advancing construction, in spite of detractors ; his children were well placed, his eldest was married ; his daughters would be soon, even without a dowry. On the other hand, this rapid ascension implied the making of enemies. Even Colbert, who supported him at the start, was to change his attitude and show distrust that wounded him : at the time of the second contract Colbert wrote to De La Feuille, telling him to watch *"this man who could cause harm to the state"*.

In a letter dated from the 6th of May 1671, De Froidour, the lieutenant-general of the Leasing of La Fère, and also Commissioner in Languedoc for the reform of Waters and Forests, describes the climate in which Riquet was working : he reported that the Canal was almost completed from Toulouse to Naurouze, but that many people were speaking ill of him out of jealousy ; that Riquet had to contend, with the censure of those who predicted the failure of the project, with the anger of the expropriated who felt they had been underpaid, and with the routine of those against innovation. Faced with the technical success, all the venom was turned towards the work, and gossip was rife with maliciousness.

Riquet was, already at the time, verifying the rule that estimates are always under-estimated and exceed the original quote through imponderables. He would go even further, never hesitating to start over some work if he thought of some improvement. Nothing was mediocre ; he would only use noble materials, multiplying the work, adding to the length of the course. He was creating for the centuries to come. Everything was perfection in simplicity.

With this attitude, within a year he had already sunk his entire resources in the project. He sold off his property, starting with the hotel in Toulouse, then the family home in Béziers. He added to his credit by obtaining, from the King, the Gabelle farms of Languedoc and Roussillon and Cerdagne for a duration of ten years. He solicited Colbert for these extraordinary and unexpected expenditures, but funds took their time to appear, and liquidation was behind the demand.

Riquet, also, was accumulating ventures. He was already contractor, for the first part of the works, from the Montagne Noire as far as Naurouze (the Mountain Channel, the Plain Channel and the damn of Saint-Ferréol), and from Toulouse to Trèbes ; of the second part, from Trèbes to the pond of Thau ; and for the construction of the port of Sètes.

St-FERRÉOL (Montagne Noire). - Les Voûtes, la Voûte d'Enfert et la Voûte de Vidange,
départ des Eaux pour Naurouze, distant de 38,077 m.

He had, it is true, established financing plans, but as always with bureaucracy, the funds arrived at irregular intervals and the engineer's accounting haste ended in the loss of Colbert's trust. Colbert, who will then go so far as to minimize Riquet's role in the construction of the Royal Canal !

The intendant d'Aguesseau, who was "living" the construction of the canal, and participating in the studies, defended Riquet ; calumny was accusing him of enriching himself with the canal whereas actually it was his financial ruin.

Riquet's answer was that of the man of action : he doubled his activity to finish his current work. But this could not re-establish his financial status. Colbert went against his distrust and intervened with the States to loan him 300 000 pounds.

In 1680, the instigator of this grand enterprise drew up his will. He died in Toulouse on the 1st of October 1680 in his Frescati home, frustrated of the supreme reward that would have been the inauguration of the Royal Canal of Languedoc in the presence of the King.

Irony of fate, there was only a league left to be dug when death took him. He was 71 ; he was 57 when he embarked upon this vast construction. Given that the life expectancy was of 40 years at the time, it was an old man who had led this work which still forces admiration today. Without the money worries that plagued him we can suppose that he would have lived to be a hundred.

III
THE ROYAL CANAL OF LANGUEDOC

The birth of a project

In his youth, Riquet had had knowledge of various canal projects, in particular, that of Arribat.

Living as he did in Revel, he was also familiar with the region : Naurouze, the Black Mountain, the forests of Ramodens and La Loubatière. This mountain is a true water reservoir. Villages bear such names as, Arfons (from the Latin Arafontium) owning twelve fountains on its land, Septfons[3] or Fontbruno[4]. Many rivers on the mountain never run dry : the Alzeau, the Bernassonne, the Lampy, the Coudrier, the Cantemerle, the Rieutort, all affluents of the Fresquel, itself running into the Aude, and on the other side of the mountain, the Sor, that wells up in the beautiful forest of Crabemorte[5], heads towards Castres, passing between Revel and Sorèze, then running into the Agout, later joining the river Tarn. Above Revel, the Sor captures the waters of the Laudot, giving birth to the site of the basin of Saint-Ferréol. It is sad to see the insufficient rainfall since 1990 paralysing the canal, in spite of the holding lake of the Cammazes.

Riquet, who had a taste for Mathematics and Science, had visited the canal of Briare, completed in 1642. Previous projects had demonstrated that the canal was feasible. Only the water was lacking. Riquet knew that it was there, inside the mountain, and all that was left was to find the exact point of separation of the waters, which was close by, and to bring the water to that spot to feed the two branches of the canal : west towards the Atlantic, and south-east towards the Mediterranean. It was thus unnecessary to try for an impossible alimentation from the Ariège.

A stroke of genius it has been said. Yes, a stroke of genius that made Riquet the unquestionable inventor of the canal, without which all previous attempts had failed.

Riquet explored the Black Mountain, noting down the debit of the various rivers and streams, the slopes of

3. Sevenfountains.
4. Brunofountain
5. Deadcrab forest.

the hills. There was water, and lots of it, but not running in the right direction. It had to be collected and directed, diverted towards the separation point at Naurouze.

Legend would have it that near the village of Montferrand there is a mass of isolated rocks, the stones of Naurouze, split in two, they will join together at the end of the world, or so Nostradamus would have it in his prophecies. The fountain of La Grave runs out of this site. While Riquet was watching the debit of this spring, a stone is said to have come unstuck and made a small dam ; the waters ran off two directions, towards the Ocean, and towards the sea ; this would have been the confirmation of the spot that Riquet was looking for.

It was then to this point that the waters had to be led, all the waters, from both sides of the mountain of Revel. The engineer's knowledge of the terrain enabled him to conceive a channel that would run along the side of the mountain and, from the southernmost and highest river, the Alzeau, allow him to gather together the other affluents of the Fresquel and send them into the Sor on the other side of the mountain. It was then possible to direct the Sor onto the Mediterranean slope, bypassing Revel, and from there, to lead it through another artificial channel to Naurouze. On this same slope flowed the Laudot, whose debit could add to that of the channel below Revel. From the Alzeau to the Sor, this channel became the Mountain Channel ; the one leading from Revel to Naurouze being the Plain Channel. The Laudot, damned by a road in the valley of Vaudreuil, was to become the damn of Saint-Ferréol.

Riquet then started experimenting in his new home of Bonrepos, building models. Of course these ideas were the result of generations of research, Riquet was able to apprehend them in a magnificent synthesis to resolve his problem.

He then applied himself to the laying out of the canal's itinerary. From Naurouze to Toulouse, the terrain presented no particular difficulties ; from Naurouze to the Mediterranean, the route was more uncertain : should he follow the river Aude, descending to the Robine of Narbonne, or else push ahead to the Lake of Thau, behind the mountain of Sète ?

Being a successful businessman, Riquet thought about the necessity of this canal, of the services it would render to commerce : time would be saved for transport, avoiding the 700 league maritime route, safety, also, would be guaranteed, avoiding gales, the Gibraltar straits, zigzagging along the coasts under the Spanish canons and attacks from pirates, still frequent at the time around French ports. As a man familiar with numbers, he calculated that a 3000 kg. load travelling on land required 6 harnessed horses and two drivers. The same traction and personnel, when applied to a boat, allowed the transporting of a 300 000 kg. load. A 200-man salary and the food and upkeep of 600 horses could thus be saved. To support his demonstration, he also calculated that : one horse walking ten hours a day, could carry a 100 kg. load, when harnessed to a cart, the same horse could haul a 1000 kg. load. Harnessed to a barge, it could haul 60 000 kg. This proved easily that transport by canal was definitely the most economical for goods.

But Riquet also knew that a construction of this scope would only see the light of day if he could produce solutions for the financing of the operation, the real obstacle remaining the lack of credit, in the absence of an organized banking system. It was thus a long-thought-out project, when at last he produced it.

1662 ; Riquet is between 53 and 58 years old. He must now hurry, for a project, using the river Agout, has been proposed to the authorities of the region : Monsieur d'Escorbiac, Counsellor in the Chamber of Edicts of Castres, has just gone up the river, accompanied by Officers of Navigation, to reconnoitre the work to be done. The project was not viable, the Agout being un-navigable, and met with strong disapproval from the inhabitants of the area.

Embarking on the Adventure

Riquet was acquainted with the new Bishop of Castres and Archbishop of Toulouse, Archbishop d'Anglure de Bourlemont, who was also one of Colbert's counsellors ; he told him of his project while he was staying at Bonrepos. The next day Riquet accompanied the Archbishop to the sites of Revel and the Black Mountain, and convinced by the rigor and clarity of the project he officially advised Colbert of the plan.

Everything started with the long letter, dated 15th of November 1662, that Riquet addressed to Colbert. In it he evokes the already long-standing necessity of the canal, for the development of trade, and the better circulation of goods, that would in turn generate profits for the King. He indicates that he has already found riverways that would be suitable for the establishment of the canal and locks. He describes precisely the water-resources of the Black Mountain, the means of using them and diverting them to the threshold of Naurouze.

Colbert was only waiting to be convinced, and had no trouble in convincing the King. In a ruling of the Council on the 18th of January 1663, he ordered the examination of the project by commissioners. The ball was rolling. The bureaucratic formalities were accomplished with remarkable speed and efficiency.

Encouraged by this first result, Riquet hurried to pursue his studies. Thus, in a letter of the 29th of May 1663 to Archbishop d'Anglure, he confirmed that he had checked his plans and calculations, and that nothing had been overlooked. D'Anglure then honored him by introducing him to Colbert himself, to whom he laid out the project during the course of an interview. He also did this with Bourgneuf, in Toulouse.

On the 8th of November 1664, the commission met in Toulouse and immediately designated experts to travel to the fountain of La Grave, at Naurouze. In their report they confirmed that it was possible to bring the water to this point, at an altitude of 50 metres above the Garonne, and that water could be found in sufficient quantities to feed both branches of the canal. Then a visit to the Black Mountain, where Riquet convinced them of his plan to capture the water.

The commissioners then preoccupied themselves with the way to follow to the Mediterranean. The river Aude was abandoned, too uncertain for navigation, and the Bishop de Bezons chose to direct it towards the Étangs of Vendres and Thau.

On the 19th of January 1665, the commission gave a favorable opinion, on the condition that a trial channel should be built. Only two years had passed since the Council ruling. Knowing Riquet, one may imagine his anxiety and exaltation. He could already see a canal that was accessible to galleys, going as far as the Rhône. In May 1665, he met Colbert once again and obtained patent letters on the 27th of the month, to start the digging of the trial channel. He began the work under the control of Bazin de Bezons and Tubœuf.

In October, the channel had been completed and Colbert congratulated him, seeing that : *"Higher than your hopes, your work has been even more successful than you had promised yourself, and that there is now none who is not persuaded of the possibility of the grand design that gives me great pleasure".*

Riquet was not blinded by success and did not lose sight of the essential point, the financing of the project. He had just advanced 50 000 pounds from his own pocket for the trial channel. On the 28th of September 1665, he proposed to Colbert that he should draw up an estimate of the cost of the work, for the water stores and diversion canals as well as the main navigation canal, and publish this estimate, without bidding, proposing to find solutions to save the king's money.

Louis the XIVth designated a famous engineer, the Knight of Clerville, General Superintendent of Fortifications, to draw up the estimate.

Given the savings proposed by Riquet for the course of the Mountain Channel, the estimate was one of 3 667 605 pounds. It didn't cover the complete length, but the length from Toulouse to Trèbes, as well as the work on the Black Mountain itself.

This was the "first enterprise", nowadays, we would say the first phase of the work. The second enterprise had not yet been finalized, the outlet onto the Mediterranean still unclear between La Franquy, La Nouvelle and Sète.

The canal of Briare had been entirely financed by its promoters, M. Boutheroue and Guyon. The cost of the Canal Of The Two Seas was too high for Riquet to be able to take it on his own ; the State coffers likewise. The absence of a banking system did not allow the setting up of a corporation as would be done today. Colbert could not but be interested in Riquet's proposals. Firstly, he was proposing to take the full cost of the first section (3 630 000 pounds !) upon himself. After the publication of the Knight of Clerville's

estimate, the rival offers were at 5 000 000, 4 540 000, and at best 3 677 000 pounds. His was thus the lowest offer, in return for which he requested :

– The use of the Farms and Gabelles of Languedoc, Cerdagne and Roussillon, for 10 years, on the same conditions as the current farmers. A use for which he offered 1 000 000 pounds, payable over eight years and used for the paying of the works. He still remained indebted to the farms themselves, for a sum of 2 135 000 pounds for the Languedoc and 75 000 pounds for the Roussillon. The million pounds only being the price of the subrogation.

– The price of the sale of the offices of salt retailer for 530 000 pounds.

– The resale of the right of "septain" for 100 000 pounds.

– The attribution of 5 sols per unit of salt, or 600 000 pounds.

– He also was buyer for the fief of the first enterprise for 150 000 pounds and of the right of way for 50 000 pounds.

For the rest, that is to say 1 200 000 pounds, Riquet was counting heavily on the States of Languedoc, the Province being the primary beneficiary of the canal.

Seeing the success of the first enterprise, and cognizant of the advantages that the canal would bring, the States granted, on the 1st of March 1667, a free grant of 2 400 000 pounds, to be paid over eight years of 300 000 pounds each. During the wait, faced with the weakness of the States, the King took recourse in the usual expedients : the selling of offices and the creation of taxes.

October 1666. The King decided on the construction of the canal in the Edict of Saint-Germain-En-Laye.

On the 7th of October, a decree of the Council of State, and the patent letters interpreting the Edict, declared that the contractors of the fief and toll, would enjoy them in all property, incommutably, which is to say that they would become owners, the goods being neither a national domain, nor subject to repurchase. In return for which they had the upkeep as permanent responsibility. Here again, the King followed Riquet's suggestion as, *"the particular interest of the owning family is best guarantee of the general interest"*. His descendants never failed in their obligations.

One cannot really say that this was a truly correct leasing of contract, but in this way Colbert could save appearances.

The Entrepreneur

So, Riquet is now an entrepreneur. The work and financing was to be spaced out over a period of eight years. Riquet, through his energy and sense of organization, will have almost finished the construction within five years ! This helps to explain the tardiness of payments and his eternal need of money, especially after the start of the second phase of construction of the canal.

He was not slowed by this work ; he hired workers and, in his haste, opened more than one construction site at the same time : the channels and the workshop of Durfort. He began organizing : each workshop would contain 200 men, divided into groups of 40, each group under the orders of an overseer, and directed by an inspector. At the start he hired about a thousand workers. When he embarked on the second enterprise, from Trèbes to the Lake of Thau, and on the third phase of construction of the port of Sète, he would have at times up to 12 000 men and women under his orders !

His organization had to change and adapt according to the expanse and dispersal of the different worksites, and the number of workers. It is easy to imagine how strictly the states of salaries had to be kept up to date, when faced with the scattered and variable armies of workers at any given time. In 1667, the number of workers was 2 000 men ; 1669, 5 000, then 7 000 and 1 000 women. The vendanges, the harvests made holes in the workforce, but in November : 8 000 men and 1 500 women.

Recruitment mainly took place amongst agricultural labourers, forming the legions of road workers digging and loading, women working more particularly at carrying the earth on their backs or in litters. To this must be added the skilled artisans and labourers who were to intervene : builders, stone-cutters, carpenters, iron-mongers, saddlers and ropemakers. Though the number of workers varied according to season and agricultural work, the army was only called on twice. Posters, put up all over the streets of the Capital, invited labourers to come and work on the canal. To attract workmen, Riquet never hesitated to propose salaries that were judged prohibitive for the period. These high salaries provoked a general outcry amongst the high and mighty such as the Bishop of Castres : *"We have had the workmen for 10 sols a day, instead of Mister Riquet on his channel, giving 20 and then 15 to gratify his friends who have found certain pleasures in it"*.

Riquet also comes across as a pioneer in social matters. He only hired those who were fit and, to speed up the hiring, in an eternal search for efficiency and productivity, he installed monthly salaries, along with a form of social security.

PLAN

PROFIL et *ÉLÉVATION*

de

L'AQUEDUC DE St AGNE.

Département de la Haute-Garonne.

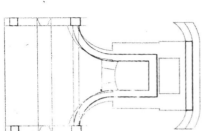

Plan

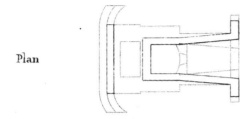

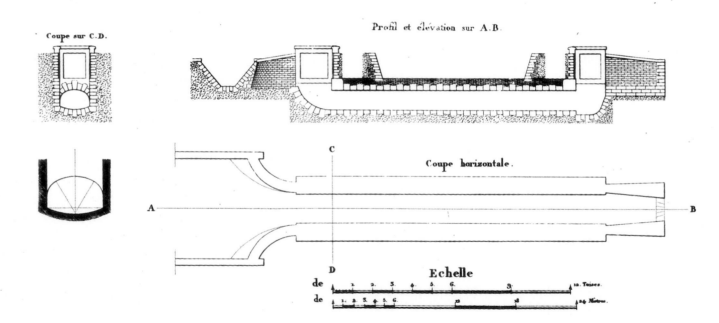

Coupe sur C.D.

Profil et élévation sur A.B.

Coupe horizontale.

A

B

C

D

Echelle

de

de

In peak periods, he called up the troops ; on two occasions, he had 600 men sent to him. He only ever had any real difficulties with the master-masons, and wagon-drivers who tried to apply exagerated prices and refused their services if the pay wasn't what they asked for. Various measures were taken — requiring them to work, with 50 pound fines if they refused — but these sanctions remained relatively ineffective.

Riquet's needs obliged the owners of saw-mills and blacksmiths to work for him in priority. He was authorized to use gunpowder, to open sand and stone quarries, and smithies ; his needs in iron led him to acquire the farm of domanial rights on iron arriving from the forges of Languedoc, Roussillon and Cerdagne.

With all this, everything was moving at a steady pace. On the 15th of April 1667, the placing of the first stone of the basin of Saint-Ferréol took place in great ceremony, in the presence of the Archbishop d'Anglure, de Montpezat and two intendents. On the 17th of November 1668, placing of the first stone of the lock onto the Garonne, the canal already open from Toulouse to Naurouze since the month of May. The filling of the canal took place in 1670. By 1672, navigation was beginning, three times a week, from Toulouse to Naurouze.

The stretch that led from Naurouze to Trèbes through Castelnaudary was only completed in 1673, due to the bypassing of Castelnaudary, and the refusal of Carcassonne to help finance the work.

The greatest construction of the century

From 1667 onwards, Louis the XIVth was absorbed in wars. Expensive campaigns imply a lack of money that paralyzes the economic life of the country, and the large construction works.

In spite of this unfavorable conjuncture, Riquet was studying the setting up of the second phase. The success of the first phase and his conceptions gave weight to his subsequent proposals. The measuring was completed, as well as the estimates. The course of the canal has been decided on : it will avoid the Aude and lead to the basin of Thau as Riquet had predicted. He had even found the means to finance the work.

In January 1668, Riquet had travelled to Sète, to check the work on the port, ideal terminus for the canal. The Province felt that the work was not going fast enough. On the 30th of June 1668, the Knight of Clerville finished his estimate and the schedule of conditions for the second phase of construction and the port of Sète. Auctioning of the contract took place in Montpellier on the 25th of November. This time it would seem that the procedure went according to rule, but Riquet held the strongest position. On the 10th of December, an entrepreneur, Jean Farrand, made an offer that he then retracted and produced again on the 17th ; he proposed to finish the work in eight years, from the 1st of January 1670, for the sum of 6 232 000 pounds. Louis Ponthier proposed the sum of 6 182 000 pounds. On the 31st of December, Pierre-Paul Riquet proposed his services and an estimate of 5 832 000 pounds, over 8 years. On the 23rd of January 1669, de Bezons accepted Riquet's offer.

Riquet was also declared contractor for the third enterprise for 1 080 000 pounds. He brought the

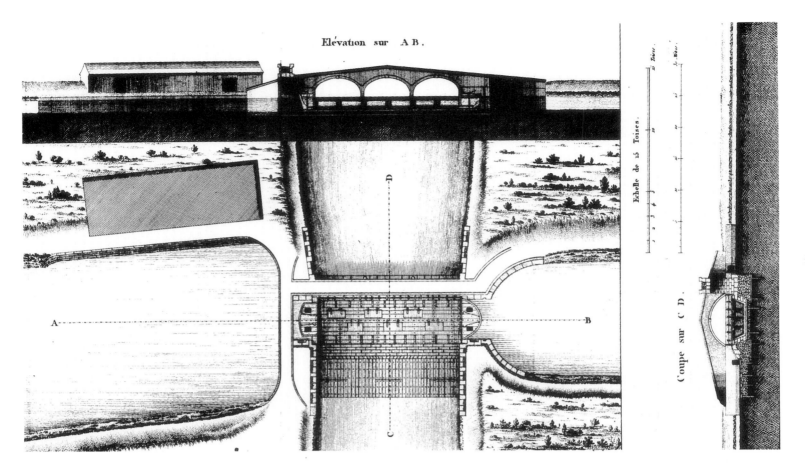

80 000 pounds by buying the fishing rights of the port of Sète and of the canal as far as Thau. The lacking million was to be taken by allocation from the Gabelles and treasuries of the States. This method of financing was not as rigorous as the first ; the methods of payment and non-respected dates of settlement attest to Riquet's permanent debts and difficulties.

So, Riquet was now in charge of building the whole of the canal and the port of Sète. Such construction attracted the attention and curiosity, not only of the French, but of various foreigners, such as the Prince of Denmark who visited the worksite in June of 1669.

A few numbers will demonstrate Riquet's immense work :

– Length of the Canal : 240 km.

– Width at the mirror (water level) : from 16 to 19 m.

– Depth : 2 m.

– Excavations : 7 000 000 m³ of earth, all manipulated by hand.

– 80 km. of channels, including 103 works, amongst which the Saint-Ferréol Barrage, clearing a 394 m. difference in level.

PLAN, PROFIL ET ÉLÉVATION DES VOUTES DU BASSIN DE S.ᵗ FERRÉOL.

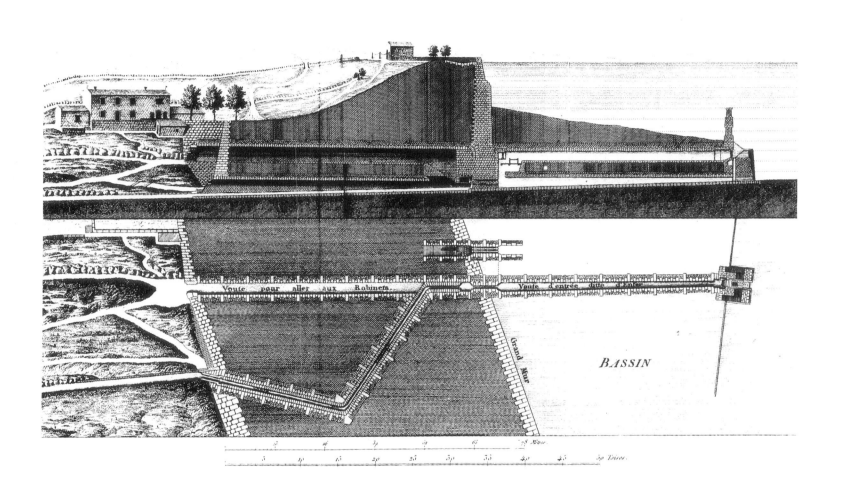

Voute pour aller aux Robinets.

Voute d'entrée dite d'amont.

Grand Mur

BASSIN

CASTELNAUDARY — Les Ecluses vues d'aval

G. Linétruy, éditeur

The Dam of Lampy was only built in 1782, to feed the junction canal to Narbonne, built between 1777 and 1787. The piercing of the Cammazes was executed by Vauban in 1686.

– From Toulouse to the Basin of Thau there are no less than 328 works : basins, bridges, aqueducts, spillways, tunnels, bridge-canals.

– Single, double and triple locks, even octuple at the arrival of the canal at Béziers, at Fonsérannes :

– From Toulouse to Naurouze, 16 locks clearing a difference in height of 57 m.

– From Naurouze to the Basin of Thau, 48 locks, clearing 189 m.

– All in all, 64 locks, including the octuple lock at Fonsérannes, a quadruple one at Saint-Roch (Castelnaudary), 4 triple locks, 19 double and 39 single locks, including the circular lock at Agde.

– A 53 km. reach, in the Minervois.

– 45 000 trees planted after completion, to hold the land along the canal banks.

In the port of Sète :

– Completion of the 1 250 m. of breakwaters, each being 60 to 70 m. wide at the base, 30 to 35 m. wide at water-level, 15 m. at the crown, 5 m. above water-level.

And how many innovations ! the originality and artfulness of certain constructions cannot be ignored.

The Barrage of Saint-Ferréol

To avoid a long period of inactivity during the dry season, Riquet had originally provided for 15 or 16 water-stores. The Knight of Clerville proposed to replace these basins by the damming of the river Laudot, in the valley of Vaudreuil. The lake was to have an area of 64 ha., and contain over 6 000 000 m³ of water. 1600 m. long, 800 m. wide, it now occupies an 89 ha. surface, containing 6 734 000 m³. (Alt. 342 m.)

The dam erected by Riquet was the first mass-barrage of this size built in Europe.

The waters are held back by an imposing 871 m long barrier, 35 m. high at the deepest point. The dyke is made of a cut granit wall, buttressed downstream by a huge enbankment of earth and rock to control the huge weight of water, that is itself held by another 3 m. thick wall. This construction presents a 117 m. wide base. The top part supports a 5 m. wide road. Water evacuation is carried out through two sunken galleries named Vault of Hell, and Vault of the Drum. Two other vaults are placed under the enbankment, the tap vaults, allowing one to gain access to the giant bronze floodgates bearing the names of their makers : Lepaute and Augete, and the draining vault. (These taps were made after Riquet's time, and were placed there in 1829.) A set of gates allows the running out of water when the basin is fed to its maximum. A conduct, its outlet at the bottom of the valley, produces a magnificent, 10 m. high, geyser that flows into the Laudot, itself joining up with the Plain Channel, outside Revel, at the post of the Thomasses.

An unprecedented technical prowess for the time, the Barrage of Saint-Ferréol remains admirable in its scope, the mastery of the execution and the ingeniousness of its conception. Three hundred years after its construction, it is still in magnificent state, functioning without failure, as Riquet concieved it in 1667. That year, the laying down of the first stone was done in great ceremony, on the 15th of April, in the presence of the Intendents of Languedoc and the Archbishops of Toulouse and Saint-Papoul, so as to, through vast publicity, attract the incredulous and disapproving.

Planted with magnificent trees, Saint-Ferréol remains a delightful location to walk, swim or sail.

The basin of Naurouze

At the terminus of the Plain Channel, on the water separation line plateau, Riquet excavated a basin in the rock to be used as a buffer reserve to feed the separation reach. Shaped like an elongated octagon, this basin was to sport in its centre a statue of Louis the XIVth on horseback, which never got beyond the modelling stage. Mud having slowly choked the basin, there is now a large island, embraced by the two branches of the channel.

The basin of Castelnaudary

On the original plans, the canal was to pass relatively far from the town. Always thinking of improvements and savings for the works, Riquet signed, on the 24th of May 1671, a treaty with the deputies of the town allowing that, with a 30 000 pound contribution the canal should be diverted to the foot of the town, and a port was built at the Pré de l'Etang. This large stretch of water, and its traffic, contributed heavily to the development of the town. Nowadays, the port is used for pleasure boats.

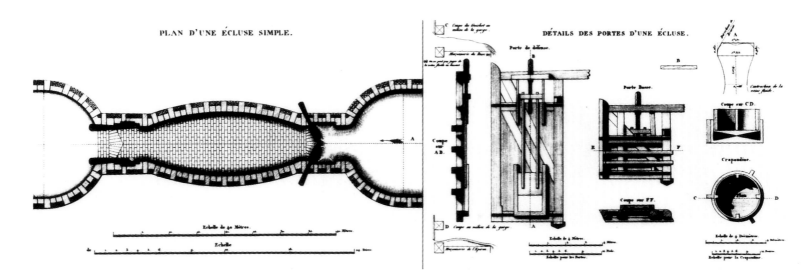

PLAN D'UNE ÉCLUSE SIMPLE.

DÉTAILS DES PORTES D'UNE ÉCLUSE.

CARTE DE LA PARTIE DE LANGVEDOC
PAR LAQVELLE SE DOIT FAIRE LE CANAL ROYAL DE LA COMMVNICATION DES MERS
ET CELLE DE LA RIVIERE D'AVDE A L'ESTANG DE THAV 1668

The locks

Riquet brought particular care to the construction of the locks, vital works in the functioning of the canal. The very first locks were built in straight lines, 40 m. long and 3,5 m. deep. They did not allow the passage of the 16 ft. wide Narbonne boats, called "capons". They were then built with curved lines, allowing for a greater holding capacity, and the dimensions were increased to 53 by 5,5 m. They were all built in hard stone masonry, well-built, they have remained the same, still in service, showing no signs of stress or of delapidation. Only the gates have been changed, now wired to an electric system.

Along the course of the canal one comes across two original locks :

– The round lock of Agde, fitted with three exits : coming from Toulouse, on may gain access to the port of Agde and the sea, or else continue on to Béziers, following the course of the Hérault for a few kilometres. This basin is unhappily no longer circular ; the enlargement for higher-tonnage barges has passably disfigured it.

– The lock of Fonsérannes. Leaving the Malpas tunnel, beside the oppidum of Enserune and the lake of Montady, the canal heads towards Béziers, flowing into the Orb, 25 m. below the level of the canal. At once, all those who wished to see Riquet's enterprise fail began maligning : "The second canal project has failed, because Mister Riquet has the head of his work buried in a mountain of sand, and at his feet two ponds that are 25 to 30 feet below his level."

In spite of his age, almost 70 years old, Riquet had kept extroardinary creative power ; he built a water-staircase, made of a series of eight majestic locks, descending to the Orb, an amazing work, 312 m. long, clearing the 25 m. difference.

The tunnel of Malpas

When Riquet's detractors wrote that he had the head of his work in a mountain of sand, they were alluding to the mountain of Enserune, close to the oppidum bearing the same name, that stood in the canal's course. This site was the end of Riquet's chosen route.

One may find Riquet obstinate. Reserving himself the right to change the layout of the canal. He had already abandoned the Knight of Clerville's route, between Trèbes and the lock of Puichéric, thus avoiding the crossing of the Aude. In the same vein, between Roubias and Béziers, he had chosen to remain in the hills rather than follow the plain, thus avoiding risks of overflowing from the Aude. Each time his correctness had been recognized. Mister Rousset, in a historical essay, illuminates the difficulties that were encountered, in particular due to the nature of the terrain, the mountain of Enserune being formed of sandy turf, water-permeable, and subject to landslides. Everyone advised that the canal should be diverted.

The split opinions provoked a cabal that alerted public opinion and reached Colbert's ears, informing him that Riquet was heading towards defeat, the peak of Malpas being nothing but a pile of sand, that would fall to pieces at the first blow of a pick. Colbert loyally informed Riquet who, true to form, replied as he had done in the past : carrying on regardless and executing. He removed teams of workmen from other sites and pierced the Malpas. With the help of Pascal de Nissan, he wooded the friable land with large beams, building as it advanced ; roadworkers, carpenters and masons all worked at the same time. Nowadays, the technique remains the same, except that the protective shield is made of steel and advances on rails.

Then the order to cease work arrived ; he again carried on, and redoubled in effort : the piercing was completed within six days. The Intendent d'Aguesseau then arrived in person, with the Commission, ordering Riquet to stop. The answer was worthy of the character, he had the amazed Commission walk the length of the tunnel, in a torchlit procession.

The final result is a vaulted tunnel, 165 m. long, with a height and breadth of 8 m., preceded by an open trench on either side. Very much ahead of his time, Riquet had created an extremely modern work, unique at the time. Other piercings of this type will only start appearing with the 19th century and the advent of the rail.

The bridge-canal of Repudre

Here also, Riquet was an innovator, inventing as he did the bridge-canal. To get across the valley of the Répudre, he had a bridge made that ran over the river, over which runs the canal, as if it were a straightfoward road. This massive construction (135 m. long) entirely built out of cut and worked stone, is still functional after more than 300 years. How many of our elegant re-inforced concrete buildings will enjoy the same longevity ?

It is impossible to evoke and describe each piece of work, too numerous to mention. From the cyclopean wall to the smallest bridge, everything was built with a sense of grandeur worthy of the century. Nothing was intended to be temporary, only noble materials were employed ; cut stone, brick, oak.

And, how much time did it take to accomplish this monumental enterprise, using picks, shovels and packs ?

Fourteen years, and no more.

The cost of the canal

Questions of money have too often been raised for us to avoid the question : how much did the canal finally cost ?

The various results are relatively coherent, whether they take into account, or not, Riquet's personal advances, never reimbursed. In pounds we find :

– Basville, in his memoirs	13 000 000
– The Encyclopaedia of 1776	17 480 000
– Delalande, "Navigation Canals" (1778)	17 500 000
– General Andreossy (not including Riquet's share)	15 622 720
– Riquet's inheritors ("History of the Canal of the Languedoc")	14 169 339
Plus Riquet's share	3 110 000
producing a result of	17 179 339

including 2 090 000 in debts

In his remarkable work, "Le Canal des Deux Mers", André Maistre has given in great detail the breakdown of expenditures, settlements and cost of constructions, with one reservation however : "It is useless to pretend on this chapter to produce rigorously exact numbers and a certain total."

In brief, and in pounds :

– The king's share	8 484 050
– The Languedoc States' share	8 070 202
– Riquet's share	2 110 109

Riquet's share is colossal for a private person. It is then far easier to understand that he not only spent his entire fortune on the construction, but also left a 2 million pound debt.

At the time of death of the "illustrious old man", the canal was almost completed, but Jean-Mathias, his son, still had to add the finishing touches to certain constructions, including the port of Sète, and already start on some upkeeping work. Unable to face the cost, his inheritors already sold almost half the proprietory shares of the canal in 1863 for a derisory sum (283 333 pounds with a possibility of repurchase) given the canal's worth, and the size of the debts.

Up to 1724, the income from the canal was swallowed up in debts and the expenditure necessary to improve the construction, after which, the inheritors bought back the sold shares so as to remain sole owners of the canal.

A note, addressed to Colbert by Jean-Mathias Riquet, shows the importance of the modifications and appreciations brought by Riquet :

– For the canal	4 481 867

– For the port of Sète	33 300

The total cost of the canal can be established at :

– The king's share	8 484 050
– The States' share	8 070 000
– Riquet's share	4 022 592
Total :	20 586 844 pounds

The sums that were doubly allocated must, however, be subtracted from this result :

– The auctions for the Gabelle farm, owed to the King, but allocated to the works	1 000 000
– Sums arriving from the revocation of the Edicts	1 983 333
– The total from the second auction of the Gabelles, allocated as above	442 483
Total :	3 425 816 pounds

The total cost of the canal thus amounts to a grand total of :

20 586 844 — 3 425 816 = 17 161 028 Pounds

CAPESTANG — Port du Canal

Edit. Aguillon

IV
POSTHUMOUS TRIUMPH

From the 2nd of May 1681, the canal was inspected along its entire length, then filled, by the Intendent d'Aguesseau, accompanied by De La Feuille, the father Mourgues, Jean-Mathias Riquet and his brothers-in-law, assisted by Andreossy and Contigny, Engineers ; then filled with water.

On the 15th of May 1681, the waters were blessed by the Archbishop Montpezat de Carbon of Toulouse.

On the 19th of May 1681, on a large state boat, the Commissioners of the King, the members of the States and Riquet's two sons inaugurated the canal, descending as far as Sète, followed by 23 other boats, coming from the Garonne and already transporting goods from the basin of Thau towards Beaucaire.

Jean-Mathias, Pierre-Paul Riquet's son, used the year 1682 to perfect the works, and, on the 28th of May 1683, a second inspection took place, entrusted to d'Aguesseau, De La Feuille and Father Mourgues by the King. It took them 75 hours to go up the canal from Marseillan to the Garonne !

Every one of Riquet's faculties had been turned towards this one aim, completing the canal as rapidly as was humanly possible and making it navigable, thus de-fusing his detractors. He knew that the slightest interruption would be fatal so, apart from the bridging of the Répudre, he satisfied himself by simply blocking the riverbeds that he encountered along the course of the canal, using the water, taking care of the most urgent problems. His inheritors put the final touches to his creation.

In 1786, the canal was diverted to pass through Carcassonne, but the work was only completed under Napoleon.

In 1810, the military engineer Niquet, taking inspiration from Riquet's influential methods, built the superb aqueduct-bridge over the Fresquel, just outside Carcassonne. The same technique was again employed at Béziers, where a bridge-canal was built in 1857 to avoid the crossing of the Orb.

In 1686, Vauban executed another piece of work upon the Black Mountain : the piercing of the Cammazes, allowing the waters of the Channel to flow, no longer into the Sor, but on the other slope, into the basin of Saint-Ferréol. Riquet had seen this possibility, but had not had the time to execute it.

In 1782, the basin of Lampy, resembling that of Saint-Ferréol, was built on the stream of Lampy to feed the junction canal with the Robine of Narbonne. Around the same time, the canal of Brienne was being excavated near Toulouse to facilitate the junction with the Garonne.

In the 18th century, Toulouse equipped itself with a second port, the port of Saint-Sauveur, the port of Saint-Etienne being too small for the developing traffic.

From 1830, the creation of a second canal running alongside the Garonne as far as its rivermouth in the Gironde was envisaged, the river presenting numerous obstacles to navigation, a solution already envisaged by Riquet and Vauban. This canal was completed in 1856 ; that is to say it took 26 years to build 193 km. A Riquet was lacking to pass over the internal quarrels and blocks : some even wanting to use the canal-bed for a railway !

V
THE LAST OF THE ROMANS

It is impossible to remain indifferent when faced with a man such as Riquet. The character is too unusual. In him were assembled such a confusion of qualities and faults that he entered, in his lifetime, into legend. In his way, like a giant.

But who was he really ?

He was certainly an extraordinarily energetic, physically strong and strong-willed man ; a remarkable financier and organizer ; an imaginative and inventive man, as well as a realist and a pragmatist. A bold and reliable entrepreneur. The canal was, for the time, a folly, but a reasoned, thought-out folly, that was supported by fact and experiment. His enthusiasm must have been communicative, to draw and convince as it did ; he was a Southerner : his volubility and exuberance must have seduced Colbert, at first. This might explain the rift between the two. The one is a man from the South, good-natured, friendly, falsely naive ; the other is a Northener, a rigorous and cold administrator. Once past the attraction of the first years, the former's methods frightened the latter. Knowing tortuous paths for having

followed them, he could not understand that Riquet's apparent straying was really just ways or expedients to arrive at the term of the work. The aim remained noble even if the paths were irregular. Especially, as the State, also, did not always hold its financial engagements on time. Riquet knew that any interruption of the work would be fatal, that was his excuse. Colbert also knew this, which is why he should not have taken the step he did when he belittled Riquet's merit in his correspondence.

The canal, especially for the second phase of the work and the port of Sète, was definitely a collective work. The Knight of Clerville, De La Feuille, Father Mourgues, Vauban, Andreossy, all brought their collaboration and their ideas to the project ; but Riquet always remained the master, finally deciding, imposing his point of view, always correctly.

It has been said of him, that he was just, fair, humane and generous, faithful to his word. His behaviour towards the workmen on the canal speaks in his favour. He was also a man who was faithful in friendship. To manage all of his enterprises he needed subordinates around him ; civil servants of the Gabelles, clerks, agents, recievers, a staff headquarters of competent people that he had been able to train and attach to himself. Certain names reappear all through the documents that mark his enterprises : Jean Mas and Jean Massias, his brothers-in-law ; Claude Delmas and Bertrand Andrieu, clerks working out of Revel ; Salastelle, a solicitor and Pierre Barancy, Lauze, Jean Baptiste Dequerre, André Lambert, Daniel Navech, appearing in both Toulouse and Bonrepos ; Etienne de Camps, Pierre Dalles ; and technicians : Pierre Campmas the fountain-maker and his son, for the Black Mountain and the feeding channel, Isaac Roux the master mason who worked on Bonrepos and the canal, Couly the innkeeper and André Lambert. Even François Andreossy, who he kept on as engineer in spite of the insolence of his publication, presenting himself as the inventor of the canal.

Was he without pride, without vanity, without harshness, neither dry, nor calculating, as some have written ? The will to succeed, to recapture his nobility and insure his children's future were too strong in him for these faults to be entirely absent ; but he never exerted them on the small and the weak. They were the corollary of the will that served his ambition, without which he would not have seen the end of his project.

Riquet did not, as any ordinary financier would have done, content himself with producing an idea and proposing the means to exploit it, leaving some firm to take the risks in his place, reserving himself the glory in the case of success, saving his stakes in the case of failure. He engaged himself totally, risking his fortune and his life, and losing both to the final success. This complete gift was his greatest merit and glory.

One must see the length of the canal to measure the grandeur of the work, a unique realization in its gigantic proportions and the perfection of its constructions. It amazed its contemporaries, including its detractors. One can see this work as the grandest of Louis the XIVth's reign, though erased and eclipsed by the splendour of the Chateau of Versailles and its new architecture. The great Vauban himself, said in a supreme homage : *"The junction canal between the seas is without doubt the most beautiful and noble of its type ever embarked upon"* and *"I would have preferred the glory of being its creator above anything I have done or may do in the future".*

The Canal of the Midi was a work worthy of Rome, leading us to say that Riquet was truly the last of the Romans ; for, after him the great constructions of this type were always the work of groups and corporations, even if, as in the case of Ferdinand de Lesseps, one man was the inventor or promoter.

Water, and The Black Mountain

The Plain of the Lauragais

A Paris coin engraved with Colbert's effigy

Riquet, Toulouse,

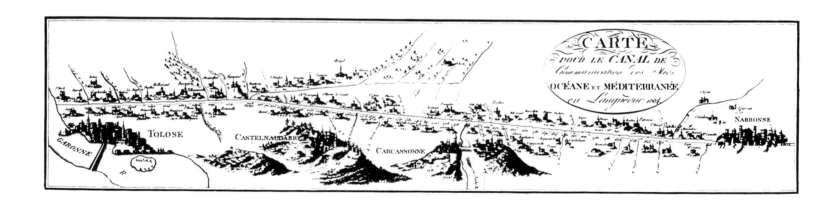

The Canal of the Midi was born of the encounter of two exceptional men : Pierre-Paul Riquet, a Gabelle farmer, and Colbert, Controller of King Louis the XIVth's finances.

The idea of a canal joining the Ocean with the Mediterranean was not a new one, but had, until then, seemed impossible, due to the lack of water at the separation point, at the threshold of Naurouze. We owe to Riquet this stroke of genius : the gathering together of the waters of the Black Mountain above Revel to feed the Canal. The waters from every river and every stream were diverged, in whole or in part, into a channel, cut into the side of the mountain and leading to the threshold of Naurouze.

The Forest of Ramodens

At the highest point, in the forest of Ramodens, at the point of capture of the Alzeau, the water starts on its great adventure.

Alzeau, the Guard-House

From the Keeper's House, it will run down along the side of the mountain, through a channel at times cut in the rock, growing larger with every stream it encounters.

54

The Mountain Channel

Above, Reservoir of the Lampy

Below, Reservoir of the Cammazes

The waters of the Lampy, later restrained by a barrage, constitute the first water store to feed the Canal, through what has been named the Mountain Channel.

Built in modern times, the barrage of the Cammazes regulates the waters of the Sor, also used to irrigate the land.

The Mountain Channel : paving on the channel-bed

In some places, terracotta paving stones were laid down on the bed of the channel, avoiding infiltration into the permeable ground.

Water capture-point of Pont-Crouzet

The waters of the Sor, arriving from the barrage of the Cammazes, are diverged in the plain of Revel, near Sorreze and Durfort, by way of the structure of Pont-Crouzet, feeding the Canal through the Channel of the Plain.

Saint-Ferréol : the dyke under high wind

Saint-Ferréol

Saint-Ferréol : water spout

The reservoir of Saint-Ferréol, holding the waters of a third river, the Audot, is closed by an exceptional dam : the first large mass-barrage of its kind to be built in Europe. It has functioned without faltering for over 300 years, the water-spray still spurting into the sunlight.

The Lake of Saint-Ferréol

The Fore-Piercing of the Cammazes

Piercing of the Cammazes : the Tunnel

The reservoir of Saint-Ferréol also holds the waters of the Mountain Channel, changing slopes as it crosses the crest, along the structure named "the Piercing of the Cammazes".

Piercing of the Cammazes

Below Revel, at the post of the Thomasses, water, arriving from the
reservoir of Saint-Ferréol and the Cammazes by way of Pont-
Crouzet, comes together to form the Channel of the Plain, which,
along a thousand picturesque twists and turns, will bring the water
as far as the threshold of Naurouze, the water separation-point.

Revel

The Channel, on the plain towards Naurouze

The Channel of the Plain

Raised in 1825 by Riquet's heirs, an obelisk perpetuates the memory of this victory for man over the elements that he put to his service.

Naurouze : the water separation-reach

The water separation-reach at Naurouze : one part will run down towards Toulouse and the Atlantic, via the Garonne ; the other heading for the Mediterranean by way of Narbonne, Agde or Sète. Dead leaves are often to be seen, spinning in the current, hesitating on which direction to follow.

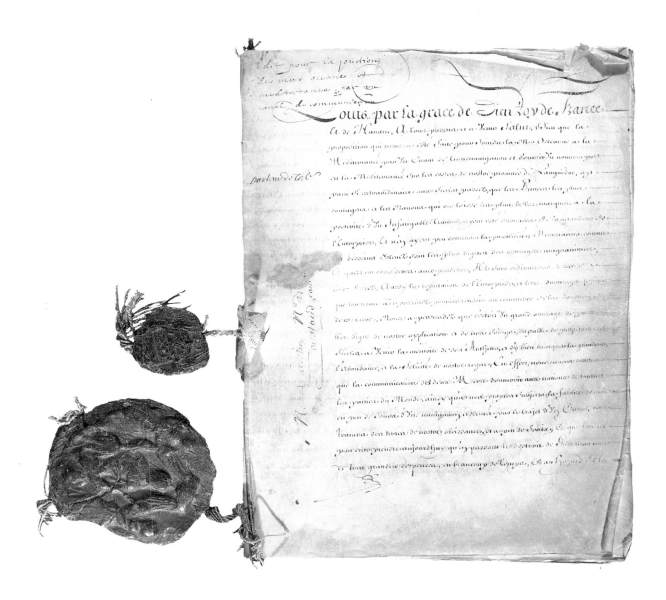

Having found the water that was at last to allow the building of the Canal, Riquet was able, thanks to Colbert's support and to the Edict of Saint-Germain signed by the Sun-King in 1666, to embark upon and almost complete this 240 kilometre-long canal ; exhausted and bankrupt, he was to die six months before the completion of the work, continued by his son after his death.

Toulouse

The boats sailing up the Garonne could not get any further upstream because of the Mill of Bazacle road. They would head into the Rivermouth basin, through a lock, that has now disappeared.

Toulouse : the Bazacle

Toulouse, the Twin-Bridges

Toulouse, the canal of Brienne

The lateral canal towards Bordeaux

The Rivermouth basin and the Twin Bridges.
The basin, also, has been radically reshaped, following the work on the bypass interchange.

The Twin Bridges, built around 1774, are placed at the start of canal that runs alongside the Garonne towards Bordeaux (1838-1852), and the canal of Brienne (1770-1776), allowing boats to head upstream beyond the Mills of Bazacle.

This Carrara marble bas-relief (1775) is the work of the Toulouse sculptor François Lucas. It represents Occitania directing the Canal towards the Mediterranean and the Atlantic.

Toulouse, Matabiau station

Through the town, the Canal and its locks (Béarnais, Minimes, Matabiau, Bayard) lead to the Port Saint-Etienne, the Port Saint-Sauveur and to the dry docks of the Pont des Demoiselles. The docks are sheltered by framework dating back to the time of construction.

Toulouse,
Port Saint-Etienne

Toulouse,
dry dock sheds

74

Toulouse dry docks

*From Toulouse to Villefranche-de-Lauragais
and Naurouze*

On the outskirts of Toulouse, the recently-built Port Sud, its marinas and pleasure-boats.

A mirror of water that remains the same though shifting all the time, the Canal offers a perpetually-changing view.
The Canal leading to the lock of Vic.

The locks : Castanet, Vic, Montgiscard, Aiguevives, Sanglier, Négra, Laval, Gardouch.

The Basin of Villefranche de Lauragais, Renneville, Encassan, Emborel, the Ocean Lock.

Between Toulouse and Castelnaudary

Calm and fresh in the summer, the Canal also reflects the thousand hues of autumn.

Montgiscard

The canal
towards the lock and Vic

Then, sometimes, the enchantment of ice and snow produces a charm-laden view.

Naurouze, the Ocean Lock

The Lock of Roc

The Lock of Béteille

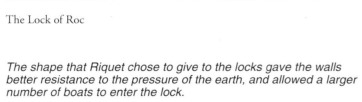

The shape that Riquet chose to give to the locks gave the walls better resistance to the pressure of the earth, and allowed a larger number of boats to enter the lock.

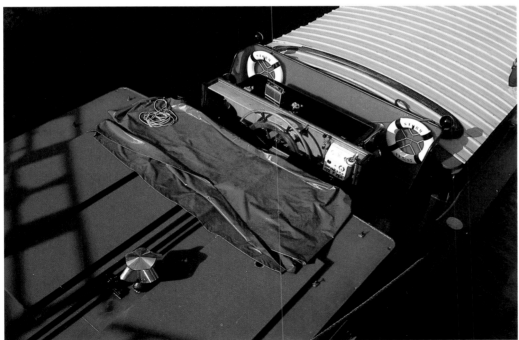

A commercial artery, the Canal had its place in Colbert's plan for the expansion of trade and industry.

Villefranche-de-Lauragais

Traffic more or less continued until 1975, conveying the wine of the Midi. Since then, canal transport has slowly faded.

Naurouze : the separation-reach for the waters arriving from the Channel of the Plain, and heading towards the Ocean lock and the Mediterranean lock.

But the Canal still remains a privileged route for pleasure-boating. The variety of the scenery, the calm and the greenery, the prestige of the towns that it flows through, all contribute in making the journey into a nautical and cultural, as well as gastronomical, joy.

*From Naurouze to Castelnaudary
and Carcassonne*

The change in vegetation starts to make itself felt.

The locks : the Mediterranean, Roc, Laurens, La Domergue, Laplanque, Castelnaudary, Saint-Roch, Gay, Vivier, Guillemin, Saint-Sernin, Guerre, La Peyruque, La Criminelle, Tréboul, Villepinte, Sauzens, Bram, Béteille, Villesèque, Lalande, Herminis, La Douce, Carcassonne.

The Lock of Roc

Towards Castelnaudary

Castelnaudary, the port

Castelnaudary : The town owed its development and growth to the passage of the Canal and the creation of a portuary basin. The town councillors solicited Riquet, requesting him to lead the canal through the town, and contributed to the financing of the work. The basin now serves as port for a firm that leases house-boats.

Bram, the Quartering house

Towards the Lock of Guerre

Carcassonne, the Old City

Carcassonne : This town was only served later by the Canal. The lay of the land led Riquet to follow the valley of the Fresquel. In 1669, he asked the town for a 1 000 000 pound participation to re-direct the Canal's course ; this was refused. The Canal thus passed two kilometres away from Carcassonne.

Only in 1787, did the town, realizing its mistake and seeing the success of Castelnaudary, decide on the re-direction of the Canal, inaugurated on the 31st of May 1810.

Carcassonne : the port

Leaving Carcassonne

95

Carcassonne – Le Somail

The Lock of Saint-Jean

The Lock of Fresquel

Leaving Carcassonne, after the lock of Saint-Jean, the Fresquel is bridged by the Aqueduct of Fresquel, both a road and canal-bridge, inaugurated in 1810, and followed by a lock bearing the same name. The Canal then rejoins the original bed, established by Riquet. The vegetation by this time is becoming more and more typically Mediterranean.

Trèbes marks the entry into the Minervois. The triple lock of Trèbes, and the now-abandoned mills bear witness to the activity induced by the passage of the Canal.

Between Trèbes and Marseillette, as the Canal passed very close to the Aude, Riquet kept the course above the river, to prevent overflowing. It was necessary to cut into the cliff to allow the passage of the Canal.

The Outpour of Argent-Double

After Puichéric and the lock, at
the level of the village of La
Redorte, an exceptional
structure, named the Outpour
of Argent-double, was
constructed in 1693 by Vauban,
to facilitate the evacuation of
water during the rise of the
Argent-double river. The tow-
path passes over the eleven
arches of the construction.

The Lock of Jouarres

ÉCLUSE DE JOUARRES.

DISTANCES:

DE L'ÉCLUSE
D'HOMPS.
3688 MÈTRES.

DE L'ÉCLUSE
DE PUICHÉRIC.
6515 MÈTRES.

DU LOGEMENT DE LA REDORTE. 2050 MÈTRES.

The double-lock of Pechlaurier

After traversing the locks of Pechlaurier and Argence, the Canal leads to a 54 kilometre-long reach, along which the water is maintained at a constant level, with no locks as far as Béziers ; this is the "Grande Retenue".

The Repudre Bridge-Canal

A little after the village of Paraza, a historic construction is encountered : the aqueduct of the Répudre. This is the first bridge-canal to have been built in France. Given the difference in height of the two waterways it was absolutely necessary to let the river pass under the Canal. Built from 1667 onwards, it was an important construction, mobilizing more than 400 workmen. The unusual spectacle of a waterway running along a bridge fascinated Riquet's contemporaries.

103

Argens

The great reach

Le Somail : It was at this point in the journey that travellers on the post-boats would stop for the night, the "couchée". The bridge named Saint-Marcel, as well as the inn-buildings, have remained the same since 1773.

The "couchée" of le Somail

After Riquet's death in 1680, and the completion of the Canal in 1681, numerous constructions were embarked upon by Vauban, in particular to improve the crossing of the rivers, whose torrential debits were troubling navigation and endangering the Canal. Numerous outpours and aqueducts were built.

The Aqueduct of Cesse

Le Somail

La Croisade

Roubia

Vintenac

The Bridge of Saint-Nazaire

It is necessary to have navigated along the Canal to comprehend the beauty and technical nature of this work, the sense of grandeur that was typical of the time of Louis the XIVth's reign and that is encountered in Riquet or Vauban's works. The smallest bridge is built to last, admirably proportioned. All is perfection in simplicity. Everything was planned as large, durable and beautiful.

From Le Somail to Béziers

Crossing Poilhes

Le Somail the port

Branching towards Narbonne

As early as 1686, work was begun to join the Canal at Narbonne with the sea at Robine, crossing the pools of Bages, Sigean and the Ayrolle. It was only in 1796 that the digging of this branch was started, along with the building of the barrage of Lampy, on the Black Mountain.

After Le Somail, the Canal continues on its course, unhindered by locks, through the Minervois and its vineyards, through the "enfilade" of Argelier. Towns, such as Capestang or Poilhes, that the Canal leads through bear witness to the growth that was brought by traffic along the Canal.

Capestang : the port

Montady : the pools

The tunnel of the Malpas

The Canal also passes close by the historic site of the Oppidum of Enserune, from the top of which one can see the star of canals of the dried-out pool of Montady, created by monks in 1247 ; the Canal then comes up against the Mountain of Enserune, that it traverses through a tunnel.

From Béziers to the Pool of Thau

Fontsérannes : the "Dînée"

Béziers

The lock of Fonsérannes deserves an isolated description. It figures amongst the most spectacular constructions : composed of eight locks running into each other ; clearing a difference in height of 21,50 metres in a space of 280 metres. Originally this lock brought boats to the water-level of the Orb, that they would then cross to arrive at the entry of the Canal, on the other side. A reservoir placed downstream from the passage, was used to keep the level of the river constant with that of the Canal. In 1857, a bridge-canal modified this route.

116

The lowest lock is now blocked-up, and the next one was modified to allow access to the bridge-canal that crosses over the Orb. On the other bank, to compensate for the height of the aqueduct, two locks were built, the lock of the Orb, and the lock of Béziers, bringing the Canal to the level of the previous one.

Béziers, the locks of Fontsérannes

The Lock of Béziers

Towards Agde, the Bridge of the Three-Eyes

Beyond Béziers, the Canal continues through the vineyards.

Another particular construction is crossed by the Canal. To clear the coastal river Libron which, although often dry, was known for its sudden and devastating floods, Riquet created a system allowing the Canal and the river to cross, although they flow at the same level. During periods of rising of the waters, the sluicegates closing the Libron were opened and the water passed along wooden tarpaulin-covered decks, thus forming an artificial riverbed crossing the Canal. This system prevented the Libron from damaging the banks or blocking the Canal with stones and alluvial waste. Upstream and downstream constructions, functioning like locks, allowed boats to pass through.

In 1858, a complicated mechanical system replaced Riquet's find.

The canal

towards Agde

Agde : the last wooden barge

Agde : the circular lock of Agde, working like a turntable, allowed boats to be directed, either towards the basin of Thau and Sète, or else, along a short canal, towards the Hérault, the port of Agde and the sea. This lock has been modified by works of modernization that have bereft it of its charm : it is no longer circular, and the stone has made way for cement.

The circular lock of Agde

Agde : crossing the Hérault

Passing through a final lock, the lock of Bagnas, the Canal avoids Mount Saint-Loup and the promontory of the cape of Agde. Practically at sea-level, flowing through the pools, the Canal reaches the port of Onglous, now abandoned, and opens into the pool of Thau. The little port of Marseillan still bears witness to the activity that the Canal created. An 18 kilometre stretch then reaches Sète, flowing through the oyster-beds of Mèze and Bouzigues. Beyond Sète, from Frontignan onwards, the Canal of the Midi is relayed by the Canal of the Rhône, heading towards the East and Northern France.

The last lock : the Lock of Bagnas

The canal crossing the pools and Mount Sain-Loup

124

Opening into the pool of Thau

Les Onglous

Les Onglous and the pool of Thau

Printed and bound in Barcelona, Spain by Cronion, S.A.